Watteau

Drawings in the British Museum

PAUL HULTON

Published for the Trustees of the British Museum by
British Museum Publications Ltd

Cover: Study of a Woman turned to the Right, holding
up her Apron (no. 27)
Frontispiece: Self-portrait of Watteau etched by
François Boucher for the frontispiece to vol. 1 of
Figures de différents Caractères (1726)

© 1980 The Trustees of the British Museum
ISBN 0 7141 0780 8

Published by British Museum Publications Ltd,
6 Bedford Square, London WC1B 3RA

Set in Monotype Bembo by S. H. Elder (Typesetters) Ltd,
Beverley, North Humberside
and printed in Great Britain by
Balding and Mansell Ltd, Wisbech and London

British Library Cataloguing in Publication Data

Watteau, Jean Antoine
   Watteau.
   1. Watteau, Jean Antoine – Exhibitions
   2. British Museum – Catalogs.
   I. Title   II. Hulton, Paul   III. British Museum
   741.9′44   NC 248.W3

ISBN 0–7141–0780–8

Contents

Watteau pinx.

Boucher Sculp.

Watteau, par la Nature, orné d'heureux talents
Fut tres reconnoissant des dons, qu'il reçut d'elle :
Jamais une autre main ne la peignit plus belle,
Et ne la sçut montrer sous des traits si galants. C. Moraine.

Preface

The collection of Watteau drawings in the British Museum is one of the two best in existence. Though slightly outnumbered by that of the Louvre, which contains finer examples of one or two of the categories of drawings mentioned below, the British Museum collection is on the whole higher in quality.

The drawings have been acquired piecemeal over a period of more than a hundred and fifty years. The first came with the Payne Knight Bequest in 1824, but twenty years were to elapse before the purchase of four further drawings, including one of supreme quality without recorded provenance (no. 27). Others were added by degrees, and it was not until 1891, when the famous collection of Miss James came on the market, that we were able to acquire at one coup seven outstanding examples for £300. A further half dozen from the same collection later found their way into the Museum. But the richest direct source of Watteau drawings was the collection of John Malcolm of Poltalloch purchased in 1895. This provided no fewer than thirteen. Another twelve came with the bequests of Henry Vaughan and George Salting in 1900 and 1910. Since then additions have been fewer, but the last – the *Design for a Fan-leaf* (no. 6), acquired from Mr Evelyn de Rothschild in 1965 – is one of the finest, and unique of its kind. The most romantic acquisition was perhaps that of *A seated Man playing the Violin* (no. 25) which was found on a barrow in the East End of London by a local man, Mr William Rodgie, who generously presented his discovery to the Museum.

An exhibition of the Watteau drawings in the British Museum is long overdue, for this is the first time within living memory – and possibly even the very first time – that they have all been shown together.

Thanks are due to the Director and Visitors of the Ashmolean Museum and the Director and Syndics of the Fitzwilliam Museum for their generosity in lending four drawings to the exhibition (nos 5, 15, 56, and one by Bernard Picart not included in the catalogue) which throw additional light on Watteau's achievement as a draughtsman.

J. A. Gere *Keeper, Prints and Drawings, British Museum*

Works referred to in abbreviated form

Adhémar	Hélène Adhémar, *Watteau, sa Vie – son Oeuvre*. Paris, 1950.
Camesasca	Ettore Camesasca, *The complete Paintings of Watteau*. London, 1971.
DV	Émile Dacier & Albert Vuaflart, *Jean de Jullienne et les Graveurs de Watteau au XVIIIᵉ Siècle*. 4 vols. Paris, 1921–29.
FddC	Jean de Jullienne, *Figures de différents Caractères, de Paysages, et d'Études dessinées d'après Nature, par Antoine Watteau*. 2 vols. Paris, 1726–28.
G	Edmond de Goncourt, *Catalogue raisonné de l'Oeuvre peint, dessiné et gravé d'Antoine Watteau*. Paris, 1875.
HV	Jacques Hérold & Albert Vuaflart, *Notices et Documents biographiques*. Vol. 1 of DV (see above). Paris, 1929.
JCR	J. C. Robinson, *Descriptive Catalogue of Drawings by the Old Masters, forming the Collection of John Malcolm of Poltalloch, Esq*. 2nd edn., London, 1876.
K der K	E. H. Zimmermann, *Watteau, des Meisters Werke in 182 Abbildungen*. (*Klassiker der kunst*). Stuttgart and Leipzig, 1912.
L	Frits Lugt, *Les Marques de Collections de Dessins & d'Estampes*. Amsterdam, 1921. *Supplément*. The Hague, 1956.
Lafenestre	Georges Lafenestre, *Dessins d'Antoine Watteau*. Paris, 1907.
P	K. T. Parker, 'The Drawings of Antoine Watteau in the British Museum', *Old Master Drawings*, v, no. 17 (London, June 1930), pp. 1–28, pls. 1–8.
Parker	K. T. Parker, *The Drawings of Antoine Watteau*. London, 1931.
PM	K. T. Parker and J. Mathey, *Antoine Watteau. Catalogue complet de son Oeuvre dessiné*. 2 vols. Paris, 1957.

Introduction

Gersaint, the picture-dealer and friend of Watteau, for whom he painted one of his last great works, *L'Enseigne*, wrote of his 'grand facilité pour le dessein' and held that the artist's drawings were to be valued much above his paintings. He added that Watteau was often frustrated as a painter in expressing 'l'esprit et la vérité qu'il sçavoit donner à son crayon'. More in line with official thinking, the comte de Caylus, in his address to the Academy in 1748, spoke of Watteau's shortcomings as a draughtsman which prevented him from attempting anything heroic or allegorical. If the criticism seems to us misdirected, Caylus nevertheless underlined the point that Watteau's whole work was outside the academic tradition. It is true that his admission piece submitted in 1717, *L'Embarquement pour Cythère*, is a kind of allegory, but the Academy created a new category for it: that of *fêtes galantes*, the genre depicting parties of young men and women in fancy dress desporting themselves in the countryside. It is a striking fact that the Academy was willing to wait for five years for the painting, having made Watteau *agréé* in 1712. In the meantime he had filled his leisure moments drawing from nature, from old masters and from the life. Caylus also said that he made his drawings in a bound book which he turned to whenever he chose to compose a picture and that the drawings were never made with a definite composition in mind. This we know was largely true since compositional studies are rare in Watteau's oeuvre (see no. 42 below).

The very few documented facts of Watteau's life are in surprising contrast to the large number of drawings now attributed to him but as he was not in the habit of signing or dating paintings or drawings the difficulties of establishing a satisfactory chronology of his life and work are considerable. Parker and Mathey in their catalogue of 1957 list nearly a thousand drawings. They do not attempt a chronological sequence, preferring an arrangement by subject matter. Since then many other drawings have come to light and others will doubtless continue to reappear. Unquestionably Watteau was one of the most prolific of all draughtsmen, for his working career as an independent artist was not longer than about eleven years.

Most of Watteau's drawings are small figure studies, often two or more on a sheet, but usually with no compositional relationship one with another. It is worth noting that in *Figures de différents Caractères*, *de Paysages et d'Études*, the book by which Jullienne sought to perpetuate Watteau's memory as a draughtsman, the selected items are not placed together as they were drawn but each study is detached and etched onto a separate plate. Watteau used his stock of studies in rather the same way as did the editor of *Figures de différents Caractères*, reproducing the chosen figures individually in his canvases. Many of them reappear more than once in different works so that an early study is as likely to be used in a late painting as in an early one. These *commedia dell' arte* figures, musicians, old men, young men and women, children and animals are caught in every sort of unassuming attitude and drawn with precision and spirit, then re-drawn with the brush, often with little or no alteration, in one of Watteau's visionary landscapes. With the constant re-use of the same or similar figures there is a familiarity about Watteau's paintings as if the same diverse company is playing in different scenes. The theatrical simile is valid, since much of his imagery is in fact derived from the stage. Working with Gillot as an apprentice in Paris in his most impressionable early period he was constantly in touch with the theatre, with actors from the *commedia dell' arte* and other companies, and with dancers and musicians. These kinds of people he continued to portray throughout his life, or, if they were not available, he used his friends or servants, often dressing them up and drawing them as if they were unaware of his presence.

It is surprising that Watteau's drawings of the nude constitute such a small proportion of his figure drawings, since there once existed perhaps nine or ten of his paintings in which the nude figure predominated. Furthermore, in many of the *fêtes galantes* the nude, in particular the female nude, is very explicitly portrayed in the statues which furnish the gardens and parks, of nymphs and, in several instances, of Venus herself. These alluring figures contrast sharply with the modest comportment of the elegantly dressed beings who staff the landscapes. There must have been many nude studies just to account for these elements in his paintings. The disappearance of many of them may possibly be accounted for in the story told by Caylus that just before he died Watteau destroyed some of his work which in an excess of delicacy he had come to consider immodest. It was also Caylus who said that Watteau had no knowledge of anatomy and almost never drew from the naked figure. He was right in the sense that Watteau did not practice anatomical drawing in the accepted way. *Académies* in which the structure of bones, sinews and flesh are analysed in careful shading would have been totally out of keeping with what we know of Watteau's methods. Yet there is direct evidence of Watteau's understanding of anatomy, particularly in some of the surviving male nudes (none of these unfortunately in the British Museum). Of these perhaps the finest is the study in the Louvre of a man for the painting *Satyr and Nymph* (PM 515), otherwise known as *Jupiter and Antiope*, also in the Louvre. Its brilliant suggestion of form completely contradicts Caylus's statement, and there exist several other male studies by Watteau of almost equal quality. In his nude studies of women he was clearly aiming for something different. Just as in many of his studies he uses all his skill to suggest the texture and light-reflecting surface of the materials clothing his figures, he seeks here to portray the supple smoothness of the female body, rather than its structure, by a quality of line, as later Ingres and Degas succeeded in doing. Not all Watteau's efforts were uniformly successful. Perhaps his most beautiful is the drawing in the Louvre (PM 522) of a young woman, half length, seated with her arm reaching over to the right. The soft contours of the arm are suggested with the utmost subtlety. He also made a number of drawings of nude or semi-nude women, usually the same model, on chaises-longues. Two of these are in the British Museum (nos 52, 53). The latter is a study for *La Toilette* in the Wallace Collection. A recent writer has severely criticised its draughts-manship, but while there is some truth in his assertion of weaknesses in the drawing of the right leg and neck, where there could be some reworking, the image remains memorable.

If Watteau was attempting to convey something other than the structure of the female form, he treated the human hand quite differently and so characteristically that his way of drawing it almost constitutes his hallmark. Where they are not merely rapidly sketched but drawn with care, and that was usually so, his hands are articulated in fine red chalk lines sometimes to the point of skeletal configuration. Sometimes they are strong and sensitive, particularly the hands of his musicians (no. 47), and seem to have more character when drawn with the rest of the figure than when they are the subject of separate studies, beautiful as most of these are (no. 46 *recto*).

Apart from the figure studies which Watteau used as his stock-in-trade, where the play of light over the folds of dress and the postures are all important, he also made a considerable number of portrait studies and finished portraits. He was clearly interested in certain popular types when these were sufficiently distinctive, such as the Savoyard peep-show men, knife-grinders, fruit-sellers, bagpipe players and the like. It has even been suggested that he was intending a series of street-cries such as Bouchardon and others produced later. Of these highly finished 'character' drawings, the finest is perhaps the *Knife-grinder* in the Louvre (PM 489), but the British Museum possesses a particularly good example, the *Old Savoyarde* (no. 9), sitting with her marmot box beside her. It is difficult to believe that Watteau was not familiar with the work of the Le Nain brothers – he in fact copied six children's heads from Antoine Le Nain (PM 343) – for he presents his types in very much the same way and in the same strong light, without a touch of caricature, entirely unidealized, but with sympathetic understanding. If they were not done for a set of street-cries they were done for their own sake, though one of the Savoyard portraits was used in the painting *La Marmotte* (Hermitage Museum). The *Kitchen Boy* (no. 2) is an example of a similar kind of drawing, highly finished in red chalk and connected with one of Watteau's early military paintings.

When Goncourt stated that portrait drawings by Watteau were uncommon, he was presumably not thinking of these popular types, nor of many of his heads, which are so carefully observed and their personalities so skilfully suggested that they must count as genuine portraits. He presumably meant the consciously-posed likeness of which there are only very few indeed. What Watteau might have achieved in this field is suggested by the highly finished portrait of the composer Rebel (PM 926). But more expressive and convincing are the unofficial portraits, often the heads of friends and close aquaintances. A marvellous example is the sheet of *Four Studies of a Young Woman* (no. 19), where his use of two shades of red chalk and black chalk heightened with white, and his skilful use of the background colour of the paper to throw the heads into relief, gives an extraordinary effect of vitality. Here are 'l'esprit' and 'la vérité' in the finest of Watteau's drawings produced in effect like a painting. And there are other less finished examples among the British Museum Watteaus hardly less convincing, the *Negro Heads* (nos 20, 21), the *Heads of two of the Daughters of Sirois* (no. 24) and the slighter sketches of a *Young Abbé* (nos 40, 41 (?)), one of the last clearly intended for a more finished portrait since Watteau has enclosed it within a strong black framework.

On looking through the *Figures de différents Caractères, de Paysages et d'Études*, it is clear that, whatever the title may suggest, landscapes make up only a small proportion of the work. In fact, there are only 12 of them as against 339 separate figure studies. It has been said that the original of only one of these landscapes, an avenue of trees (Hermitage Museum; PM 457), has been identified. Yet Parker and Mathey include more than a hundred landscapes in their catalogue of Watteau's drawings. It may be assumed, therefore, that landscape was a much more important part of his work as a draughtsman than is now apparent, and that many landscape drawings have been lost, or remain untraced or unattributed. The landscapes in *Figures de différents Caractères* are clearly from nature, as unassuming as most of the figure studies. No doubt the popularity of Watteau as a figure draughtsman (the term Watteauesque seems to apply almost exclusively to a way of representing the human figure), accounts for the survival of so comparatively large a proportion of his figure drawings. Yet there can be no question that Watteau himself placed great emphasis on his landscape drawings, whether taken from old masters or from nature. It has been shown that he treated these as he treated his figure studies, keeping them by him for use in paintings if required. Actual examples can be cited: the re-employment in the painting *La Leçon d'Amour* (Nationalmuseum, Stockholm) of the tower and other buildings in the background of a drawing he copied from some Venetian master (Art Institute of Chicago; PM 427); and the use of a drawing he made from nature of the church, tower and houses of Gentilly (Teyler Museum, Haarlem; PM 472) for the background of *La Marmotte*. In fact, the pattern of the buildings in the latter painting is somewhat different and it is doubtful whether Watteau used the drawing directly. There is evidence that he was in the habit of making intermediate drawings which he faithfully translated to canvas. One such example is the red chalk drawing in the Metropolitan Museum of a cottage at Porcherons, the old market-garden area of Paris, where Watteau was probably living in Crozat's house. This view was re-drawn (private collection, Paris; PM 444) and then used for the lost painting *L'Abreuvoir* (DV 137). Another preliminary drawing in the Metropolitan Museum is connected with the pendant to that painting, also lost, *Le Marais* (DV 136), though the actual drawing Watteau used is not known. Another very similar to *Le Marais*, which Watteau also probably made at Porcherons, is in the British Museum (no. 7). The landscape backgrounds of his *fêtes galantes* are often heavily wooded. Horace Walpole did not admire the way Watteau painted trees – 'those tufts of plumes and fans, and trimmed up groves, that nod to each other like the scenes of an opera'– but accounted for it by discovering himself that the trees of the Tuileries and villas near Paris really were like that. It is clear from Watteau's paintings that his trees were not merely artificial furnishings for his landscapes but were the result of a genuine feeling for, and close observations of, nature. His *fêtes galantes* are visions of an ideal world where elegant and gracious beings enjoy the delights of unsullied nature and are in total harmony with it. Just as these beings were based on the most precise and spirited drawings of real people, so much of his landscape painting was based on realistic studies from nature which he was continuously observing and drawing in all its changing moods. Caylus said that besides studying and copying the finest works of Rubens in the Palais de Luxembourg, he never ceased drawing the trees in the palace gardens which, because they were less tidy than other royal gardens, offered a greater variety of views and a better chance of observing the contrasting effects of light at different times of the day. Few of the many tree studies which Watteau must have made have in fact survived, but a slight study of a tree in red chalk with washes of greenish brown (no. 12 *verso*) is one of them. His interest in the details of nature which many other landscape artists would have ignored can be seen in a landscape drawing in the British Museum (no. 11 *verso*), unusual in its medium of black chalk and black wash, and in its content, where plants and grasses, among them a careful study of a hart's tongue fern, are enlarged to dominate the skyline.

Much, then, in Watteau's paintings, where landscape is usually an important element, is a projection of real-life studies of man and of nature. But just as Claude put into his paintings architectural, and sometimes natural, features which were imagined rather than observed, so Watteau sometimes added exotic or fantastic details to his landscapes which were not taken from his own studies either of architecture or of nature. The exotic tower in *La Leçon d'Amour* has already been mentioned, but the same thing sometimes happened with natural features. Beyond the naturalistic foreground of *L'Embarquement pour Cythère* (Louvre) and the beautifully observed autumnal trees of the middle distance are the pinnacles of a distant mountain, part of the

Ile de Cythère, lit by a pale golden light. These visionary peaks were not part of Watteau's own experience, or invented as some of Claude's features were, but were taken from a drawing by some Venetian master of the circle of Domenico Campagnola. Watteau's *Fantastic Landscape* from the Fitzwilliam Museum (no. 15) has mountain peaks very similar to those in the picture, and buildings in the middle distance also like those on the mountain-side on the extreme left of the picture. The source of Watteau's drawing is not known, but Caylus engraved a similar landscape in the French royal collection then thought to be by Titian.

Contemporaries praised Watteau's landscape paintings for their charm, their pure natural colours, their delicate and varied skies (La Roque), for the mastery of colours in the backgrounds (d'Argenville), but hardly anything remains except perhaps the drawing of Gentilly (see note to no. 6), which can be considered as preparatory, so far as colour is concerned, to any of his landscapes. That Watteau maintained his interest in landscape drawing and painting until the end of his life is shown in a letter he wrote to Jullienne from Nogent shortly before his death. In this he speaks of recent paintings of Nogent, 'bagatelles' he calls them, which he promises to show his friend. They remind him of some sketches of Nogent which he believed Jullienne valued because his wife had been present when they were made and presumably admired them. No surviving paintings or drawings can be definitely associated with Nogent from Watteau's last period but it is clear that landscape was always a prime concern, at least as vital to him as the human figure.

Seven or eight years before Watteau became famous as the painter of *fêtes galantes* he had already established a wide reputation as an ornamental painter and designer. Though most of his original paintings in this genre have disappeared, his output must have been considerable, for the *Oeuvre gravé* and *Figures de différents Caractères* reproduce no less than ninety-four of his ornamental compositions, drawings and paintings, most of them engraved by Huquier. About 1707 Watteau became the pupil of Claude Audran at the Palais de Luxembourg. Audran was in charge of the decoration of the royal residences and was one of the most influential figures in the introduction of the new rococo style. He had assembled a team of artists whose chief concern was arabesques and grotesques and who each specialised in a different kind of work. Watteau was required to supply the necessary figures. There is a large drawing by him in red chalk and pencil in the National-museum, Stockholm, of a panel of arabesque ornament, with figures of monkeys feasting (PM 183) which develops a design by Audran in the same collection. Watteau's figures are more vital and also more sophisticated than those in the original drawing, for Audran was more concerned with the basic arabesque design than with its elaboration. The finished painting was delivered to the Château de Marly in 1709, which gives an approximate date for Watteau's drawing – a rare piece of evidence in the dating of Watteau's oeuvre. Audran was clearly well satisfied with his pupil's work, for he allowed him to design and paint thirty *chinoiseries*, executed after 1708, for the Château de la Muette. We also know that Watteau assisted Audran with painting *The Months* for the Château de Meudon and with other assignments. To Dezallier d'Argenville and Caylus such work was considered to have diverted him from serious art to the public's loss, and to have been a frivolous misuse of his talents. One excellent surviving example of this little-known side of his work is the *Design for a Fan-leaf* (no. 6) which could well date from the period when he was working for Audran. The unusual techniques employed in this unique and very beautiful drawing are considered below.

Watteau's activities as a draughtsman ranged very widely, more so than might be apparent from his paintings, and it is in his drawings more directly than in his paintings that his stylistic development can be followed from his earliest work under Gillot to almost his last for Gersaint. All contemporary biographers of Watteau agree in stressing the strong and lasting influence which his first true master, Claude Gillot, exercised on him. It may be seen in two ways: his predilection for theatrical subjects and theatrical postures; and his tendency to adopt and retain certain stylistic mannerisms of Gillot. Jullienne says that Watteau worked on theatre decoration when he first went to Paris, for an unnamed master. Exactly when he met Gillot (perhaps as early as 1703?), and how long he worked for him is not known. Much clearer is the Gillotesque manner of Watteau's early drawings. The difficulty of distinguishing between these and Gillot's work has often been stressed. There is evidence to show that just as Watteau seems to have derived both the idea of his *Embarquement pour Cythère* and even parts of its composition from a drawing by Gillot, so he copied and imitated Gillot's figure drawings. The fact that it is now known that a sheet of theatrical figure studies in red chalk in the Hessisches Museum, Darmstadt, formerly attributed to Gillot, is a copy by Watteau of another sheet (Woodner collection, New York) which can confidently be given to Gillot, is some evidence of the way Watteau worked at this early period of his career. Though at first sight his copies seem to follow the originals closely, there is a vitality, a lightness of touch, and a delicacy as against a stiffness, a dullness of line and a lack of precision in the Gillot. Add to these differences the entirely characteristic study of hands on the Watteau sheet which does not appear on the other and is beyond Gillot's capacity, and the distinction between the two artists is clear. In these copies certain other Gillot mannerisms are noticeable, the attenuation of the lower legs and feet, the use of long straight lines, the small reliance on hatching and the indication of features by dots and dashes. Many of these are characteristic of Watteau's early drawings and some are found even in his mature work. Though the use of sanguine alone is rather unusual for Gillot, it is Watteau's preferred medium at this early stage. Unlike Gillot, he almost never used pen and made rather little use of wash. Since he was so receptive of Gillot's ideas, it is likely that he also began to compose arabesques before he left him to work for Audran who is generally credited with having aroused his new pupil's interest in ornamental design, for Gillot produced large numbers of arabesques and grotesques. It is interesting to compare a panel of arabesques by Gillot in the British Museum containing an open pavilion, with a figure of Diana in the centre, with a design by Watteau in the Bordeaux-Groult collection, Paris (PM 191), showing a similar figure of Diana, this time under an elaborate canopy. The ornamental element is more developed in Watteau's drawing, which is executed in red chalk (Gillot's work is in pen and watercolour) and was probably made later in his post-Gillot period. The grotesque and satirical element in Gillot's work must also have appealed to Watteau, bearing in mind the latter's misanthropic nature which Caylus and others remark on. It is therefore surprising that so few of Watteau's satirical drawings survive. A sheet of three caricatured heads in the Uffizi (PM 924) drawn in strongly accented strokes of red chalk reveals a highly developed sense of satire, as does the etching by Pond after Watteau of the charlatan Dr Misaubin, the original of which must have been made in London, 1719–20.

The single most important move in Watteau's short career was to work under Charles Audran at the Palais de Luxembourg. His freedom to study the collections, which included the cycle of paintings by Rubens of the life of Marie de Médicis, now in the Louvre, was of supreme importance to his development as an artist. It is not difficult to imagine what he admired in Rubens: invention, vitality, and colouring. He made more copies of Rubens than of any other artist – there are at least thirty known – and apart from actual copies he drew compositions inspired by him, as for example the *March of Silenus* (Paris, private collection; PM 259). A copy of a detail from one of the paintings of the Médicis cycle is in the British Museum (no. 4). In this, and particularly in the sheet of studies from the same cycle in the Kramarsky collection (New York; PM 266), he has so identified himself with Rubens that, though the copies are close, the heads, drawn *aux trois crayons*, look like Watteau's characteristic life drawings. It is certain that he was familiar not only with Rubens' paintings but with at least some of his drawings. The *Head of a young Woman* in the Kramarsky collection (PM 282) must have been copied from the drawing by Rubens, now in the British Museum, or the replica in the Rothschild collection in the Louvre. His technique can come close to that of Rubens, except that he makes little or no use of pen and wash. For example, a comparison of the Rubens drawing of Isabella Brant in the British Museum and a Watteau head drawn from the life such as the *Studies of the Daughters of Sirois* (no. 24) makes the point. The use of red and black chalks side by side to strengthen the mouth, nostrils, eyes and ears is similar. It is almost as if Watteau's use of *trois crayons* has as its origin the impulse to emulate the colouring of Rubens. The drawing by Watteau of Isabella Brant (Fitzwilliam Museum; no. 5), though copied from a Rubens painting and so somewhat tentative, is

Rubensian in feeling and to some extent in technique. But Watteau did not merely find inspiration in the work of Rubens or develop his technique by copying or imitating him. He also used some of his ideas for his own compositions. A cherub (PM 264) derived from *The Apotheosis of James I* became a preparatory drawing for one of the flying cherubs in *L'Embarquement pour Cythère*. Dezalier d'Argenville adds Van Dyck's name to that of Rubens, saying that these two artists delighted Watteau by their colouring. Certainly Watteau seems to have studied Van Dyck closely and there are a number of copies to prove it. One of Watteau's most unmistakable characteristics as a draughtsman and painter is the way he emphasises the play of light on the surface of his silks and cloths and accentuates their folds. Van Dyck's portraits with their richness of dress must have dazzled him with their colour and the way their silks reflect the light. Perhaps consciously or unconsciously he was using Van Dyck as his model in his efforts to capture the same effects. Other qualities must also have impressed him, among them a kind of elegant restraint more in keeping with Watteau's own manner than with the exuberance of Rubens.

Though the opportunity to study and copy Rubens, Van Dyck and the older masters at the Palais de Luxembourg was of great importance to Watteau, the work he did for Claude Audran must also have had a strong influence in shaping his style. The large drawing in Stockholm by Watteau, already mentioned, of a panel of arabesque ornament with figures of monkeys, is probably typical of the work he was doing at this time. It is drawn with spirit and wit, with great refinement and with a strong sense of design. The figures are still Gillotesque, though superior to anything of the kind that Gillot achieved. Caylus observed perceptively that white or gilded grounds (for ceilings or walls) compel in the ornamental painter 'une légèreté de pinceau', a lightness of touch which, together with an instinctive feeling for design, remained a marked chracteristic of Watteau as painter and draughtsman.

Something of his abilities in the way of ornamental invention can be judged from the very beautiful *Design for a Fan-leaf* in the British Museum (no. 6). It is unique in that watercolours and gouache are both employed. Watteau is seeing and using the sheet as a painter, and this is a true picture. His figures are standing on a knoll against a distant landscape, their costumes painted in russet-brown, pink, blue, grey and green with white gouache used extensively. The landscape background of trees and low buildings and water is indicated naturalistically and most sensitively in grey wash with white and pale yellow heightening. Enclosing this scene is a cartouche of rococo ornament with draperies, sprays of flowers and foliage and two grotesque heads in profile. The elongated *commedia dell'arte* figures are still rather in the style of Gillot and the head of the woman wearing a *fontange* suggests an early date, of the period when Watteau was working for Audran, possibly *c.* 1708. He continued making ornamental designs throughout his career, generally in red chalk only, many of them large and looking as if they were rapidly done and all with the wonderfully light touch which is found in most of his drawings, though less perhaps in his later work.

Two sets of engravings, *Figures de Modes* and *Figures françoises et comiques*, provide a clear idea of Watteau's abilities as a draughtsman before he left Audran. The former set cannot be dated later than 1710 and contains eight figures designed and etched by Watteau almost all strengthened for publication by other engravers. These must have been originally executed perhaps several years before 1710. The latter set, though it cannot be dated earlier than 1715, also contains figures designed by Watteau but engraved by other hands and most of them clearly of the same early period as the *Figures de Modes*. The overall impression of this work and of the surviving related drawings is that of a talented draughtsman with a highly decorative sense of line, who still works within a rather stilted conception of the human figure which, though more elegantly portrayed and convincing than Gillot's figures, retains his rather stiff manner of presentation. However, *A comic Actor* (no. 13), one of the drawings relating to *Figures françoises et comiques*, reveals a more mature technique and suggests that this figure at least can be dated somewhat later.

In 1709 Watteau competed at the Academy for the Prix de Rome. Though he failed to win it, he seems to have determined to start his career as an independent artist about this time, for he left Audran and returned to his native Valenciennes. This part of France was still at war and military camps and soldiers on the march were everywhere in evidence. Watteau must have observed them carefully and it is tempting to think that he filled his sketchbook with studies of soldiers drawn from the life at this time. However, Parker and Mathey believe that all the studies (or all those that survive) preparatory to the twelve or so military paintings Watteau executed were made from a single model whom he posed in many different attitudes, even varying the physique in part when it was necessary to diversify the figures for his paintings. So began a more intensive observation of the human figure. Watteau was now able to work independently, since before leaving Paris for Valenciennes he had sold a painting of some military subject to Sirois, the frame-maker and dealer, who immediately placed an order and paid him in advance for a pendant. Thereafter he seems to have had no difficulty in selling his work. In order to be free to draw and paint as he wished he needed security, and this he found in the support of several enlightened patrons. After an absence of some months he had returned to Paris in 1710 and was given accommodation by Sirois in his house on the Pont Notre-Dame. He was on terms of close friendship with the family and was constantly using them as models. The studies he made then and during the following year culminated in the painting *Sous un Habit de Mezetin* (Wallace Collection) showing Sirois and his family in *commedia dell'arte* costume. Watteau had thus returned to the *mascarades* of Gillot but how far he had advanced technically may be seen in one of the studies for the painting (no. 24). In these he has moved away from his standard model, the woman with the clean cut features, small nose and flared nostrils to the large-nosed *Daughters of Sirois* who are presented without evasion or compromise. His use of red and black chalks in juxtaposition, so reminiscent of Rubens, combines refinement of detail with sureness of touch and sensitive modelling to produce two most convincing portraits. With the intention of widening his experience in Italy he submitted work to the Academy in another attempt to win the Prix de Rome, but at a meeting in 1712 the Academicians decided that in view of Watteau's exceptional merits he should be received as *agréé*. A visit to Italy was therefore frustrated. Little is known of his working life at this time. He seems to have enjoyed the support and friendship of the older artist Lafosse, one of those chiefly responsible for effecting the change to the new style later known as rococo. His influence on Watteau must have been considerable, and it is probable that he introduced him to the rich collector Crozat. Watteau was offered accommodation and the freedom of Crozat's collection. This must have been almost as important to him as the opportunity to study Rubens at the Palais de Luxembourg. Crozat, Treasurer of France, and immensely rich, spent much of his fortune collecting works of art, especially drawings, which he acquired in large numbers, both of the northern and of the Italian schools, in particular Rubens, Van Dyck and Rembrandt, and of the Italians Correggio, Parmigianino, and the Venetians Titian, Veronese and Campagnola. Each week, according to Mariette, Crozat invited his collector friends, Jullienne and Caylus among them, and artists and writers to come to his house to examine and discuss his collection. Watteau and Lafosse, who also lived in the Hôtel Crozat, must have attended these sessions but everything we know of Watteau makes it appear unlikely that he enjoyed these occasions though he would undoubtedly have widened his circle of contacts. Crozat's patronage certainly thrust him into the limelight but there is some evidence that he did not always welcome new commissions. He clearly placed more value on his freedom to draw and gather new ideas as he worked through the collection. A considerable number of landscape drawings made at this time lie behind the paintings of *L'Abreuvoir* and *Le Marais*, views of Porcherons, the neighbourhood in which the Hôtel Crozat was situated. The *Landscape with Cottages and Figures* (no. 7) was probably drawn then. Watteau's study of the collection provided him with the material with which to fashion new ideas of composition and imagery. He derived inspiration above all from paintings, drawings and prints of the Venetian school. Bassano and Veronese were artists he copied in addition to Titian and Campagnola. Watteau's *Jupiter and Antiope* (Louvre) is certainly Titianesque and the sleeping nymph in that composition reappears in *Les Champs-Élysées* (Wallace Collection). The very beautiful outline drawing in red chalk, *The Finding of Moses* (Paris, École des Beaux-Arts; PM 859) was clearly inspired by Veronese and shows how much Watteau was learning about composition. Dacier thinks it may have been intended as a first idea for a *morceau de reception* for the Academy but was later abandoned. Watteau's most productive period, culminating in his masterpiece *L'Embarquement pour Cythère* (Louvre), followed directly from the time he spent at the Hôtel Crozat.

The British Museum is rich in drawings in Watteau's mature style, a description which may be applied to work done after his first stay with Crozat, that is from about 1713. Only one of these drawings can positively be dated, the *Oriental Servant walking, holding a Plate* (no. 14) which is connected with the arrival of Mohamed Riza Bey and his Persian embassy in Paris in 1715. Drawn in red and black chalk, it is an impressive example of Watteau's technical advance. The old refined, even mannered, line is replaced by a more assured one. The effect is altogether stronger and more effective. It is probable that many of the drawings used for *L'Embarquement* were made within a year or two of the same date. There are no less than three in the British Museum (nos 26–8). The first and most memorable is *A Man helping a Woman to rise* (no. 28), significantly chosen by Boucher to include in his frontispiece to volume II of *Figures de différents Caractères*. Executed *aux trois crayons*, it has every appearance of having been drawn swiftly – there are *pentimenti* – and with great economy. It expresses in a wonderfully balanced line the beginning of a movement arrested for one instant. The figures, not surprisingly, are unaltered in the painting. The *Studies of two Women, one holding up her Apron* (no. 27), in red and black chalk, is less elaborate though no less beautiful and with the same 'snapshot' quality of unaffected movement meticulously observed. The *Figure of a Man holding a Staff* (no. 26) on the other hand harks back to the elegant, posed figures of Watteau's earlier period and is drawn in red chalk only. Even more characteristic of the quality of drawing which Watteau was capable of when aroused by his own particular enthusiasms are the fine studies of musicians used in paintings which can be dated close to the year of *L'Embarquement* (1717): the *Man playing a Guitar* (no. 47) for *La Game d'Amour* (London, National Gallery) and the *Man playing a Violin, wearing a Cape* (no. 25), perhaps connected with *Les Plaisirs du Bal* (Wallace Collection). More Watteauesque still is *A Woman in a Striped Dress* (no. 33) for the painting *Plaisirs d'Amour* (Dresden). It is essentially the drawing of a dress clothing a woman and is as arresting and evocative as any of his finest studies of women's heads or female figures. Not highly finished, in black and red chalks and pencil, the dress is made to convey by association the beauty and the grace of the woman whose body is only lightly indicated from behind. The ability to endow a piece of material with such meaning anticipates the revolution in artistic aims for which Watteau was primarily responsible.

When an artist dies young at the height of his powers it may seem inappropriate to speak of his last phase. Yet there is a marked change in style from the drawings just discussed to those associated with paintings of his last two or three years or which can be dated by other evidence to within that period. A point of reference is the painting *L'Enseigne de Gersaint*. Gersaint himself says that after Watteau returned to Paris in

1721 he asked Gersaint if he would like him to paint a shop-sign for his premises on the Pont Notre-Dame. Gersaint finally agreed and adds that the work was done in eight days. Gersaint was mistaken in the date of Watteau's return to Paris which was in fact sometime in the summer of 1720. It is probable that the painting was finished later in 1720. As it is one of the few for which a compositional drawing exists it is clear that the drawing cannot predate the decision to undertake the painting. The drawing (Paris, Musée Cognacq-Jay; PM 688) shows the figures of two men packing pictures into a case, though their relative position is somewhat different in the painting, for it is very much a first sketch. *Aux trois crayons*, it is made up of strong straight strokes, bare of any detail, a powerful drawing with not the slightest suggestion of that decorative quality of line so often found in Watteau. Its purpose is entirely preparatory, but it is surprising how fully the upright man holding the picture is suggested in the drawing. The drawing on the back of the sheet of *Studies of Hands* in the British Museum, of a man raising a curtain (no. 46 *verso*), is very much in the same style. There is hardly a curve to be seen and very little hatching and the red chalk lines are strongly accented. So few are the signs of 'period' in this drawing that had it been separated from the *recto* (both were used for *Les Comédiens italiens*) it could almost be taken for a product of the later nineteenth or early twentieth century. Something of this same bare, almost stark, quality is also found in the studies of hands on the *recto* of the same sheet though they are fully modelled. Three other drawings in the British Museum, all considered to be late because they are executed in a closely similar style, are the *Man wearing a Tricorne* (no. 51), *An Engraver working at his Table* (no. 54) and *Studies of a young Woman wearing a linen Cap* (no. 55). The first is a remarkably vivid portrait, the face strongly modeled with straight hatching. The same sheet contains one of Watteau's finest studies of hands, unfortunately joined awkwardly to the other, originally separate, study at some later period. The two studies of the *Young Woman* are very likely to have been drawn in England, as the paper is English, and can therefore probably be dated 1719–20. Watteau has used the background tone of the paper to the maximum effect in the modelling of the heads and the hatching elsewhere is made up of long straight severe strokes. A curious and interesting drawing in red chalk, which from its content may be dated 1720, is *Le Naufrage* from the Ashmolean Museum (no. 56). It is, unusually for Watteau, an allegory showing a man being helped ashore from a boat in a stormy sea with Neptune in attendance. The generally accepted interpretation is that Watteau has pictured himself not only being brought ashore from a rough Channel crossing but also being rescued from financial disaster by his friend and patron Jullienne. Neptune on a sea-shell harnessed to horses, and all the figures, are drawn in scroll-like lines which seem to reflect the agitation of the waves and flying spray. It is a witty and strikingly rococo composition, not entirely removed from Watteau's earlier ornamental work, but is an altogether exceptional drawing which stylistically anticipates Boucher and Fragonard.

Gersaint summed up Watteau's achievement as a draughtsman by saying, 'Pour ses desseins . . . depuis qu'il est sorti de chez M. de Crozat, rien n'est au-dessus dans ce genre; la finesse, les grâces, la légèreté, la correction, la facilité, l'expression, enfin on n'y désire rien, et il passera toujours pour un des plus grands et un des meilleurs dessinateurs que la France ait donnés.' It would be difficult to improve on this verdict. Watteau was above all a draughtsman and it is interesting to note that he drew with the brush on canvas exactly as he drew with chalk on paper, as may be seen in the offset from part of an oil painting (no. 57). The images that he made initially on paper, often in red chalk only, the more finished *aux trois crayons* achieving the effects of painting, made such a strong impression on the European consciousness as to change the direction of art in France and so in western Europe.

Catalogue

As a precise dating for Watteau's drawings is not possible the entries are listed mainly in the order of K. T. Parker's catalogues: 'The Drawings of Antoine Watteau in the British Museum', *Old Master Drawings*, v (1930); and *The Drawings of Antoine Watteau* (1931).

1 Three Studies of a seated Woman with a *Fontange* Head-dress

Red chalk; 142 × 215
Provenance Rodd. 1859-6-11-11
Literature P1, fig. 2; PM158

The drawing was formerly attributed to Lancret, but the sure touch and crisp accent belong unquestionably to Watteau. The central figure is found in another rather more skilful and mature drawing, without the head-dress, in a private Paris collection (PM170), which was etched by Watteau not later than 1710 for *Figures de Modes* (DV40). This points to a very early date for the present sheet of studies. Their attenuated style moreover suggests that the influence of Gillot was still strong.

2 Standing Figure of a Kitchen Boy

Red chalk; 187 × 117. Etched by François Boucher, in reverse (*FddC*193)
Provenance Malcolm (JCR485). 1895-9-15-937
Literature P2, pl. 1; PM254

Watteau used the study for the painting, *Escorte d'Équipages* (DV125), the location of which is not now known, but which was engraved by L. Cars in 1731. The lost original has been dated 1710–12. The comparative lack of accent in the drawing and its unusually careful finish suggest a date a good deal earlier than that of the painting.

3 Five Studies of a seated Woman seen from Behind

Red chalk; 183 × 251
Provenance Huquier (L1285); Dimsdale (L2426); Woodburn (L2584); Utterson; Robinson (L1433); Malcolm (L1489; JCR492). 1895-9-15-944
Literature P3; PM252

The figure in the lower left-hand corner occurs in *Escorte d'Équipages* (DV125) with which the preceding drawing is also connected. Other drawings related to the painting are found in the Boymans Museum, Rotterdam and in the École Nationale des Beaux-Arts, Paris.

4 Ariadne, Bacchus and Venus from the *Government of the Queen* by Rubens

Red chalk; 163 × 184
Provenance The stamp FRO (L1045) is, according to Fagan, that of a mounter of French eighteenth-century drawings. 1846-11-14-24
Literature E. Staley, 'Rubens and Watteau', *Burlington Magazine*, XII (1907), p. 164; C. Phillips, *Idem*, p. 250; L. Binyon, 'Les dessins de Watteau au Musée Britannique', *Revue de l'art ancien et moderne*, Jul.-Aug. 1921, p. 140; P4; PM263

The figures are taken from the twelfth panel of the Marie de Médicis cycle of paintings by Rubens, formerly in the Luxembourg Palace, now in the Louvre. The drawing is one of numerous copies by Watteau of the master whom he admired the most.

Staley was the first to recognise the source of the drawing. Other rare drawings from this cycle are found in the collection of D. H. Gordon, Baltimore (PM258) and of S. Kramarsky, New York (PM266).

5 Portrait of Isabella Brant, after Rubens

Red, black and white chalks; 186 × 127
Provenance Mayor (L2799; Ricketts and Shannon. Reg. no. 2267
Literature Vasari Society facsimiles, 1st series, V (1909–10), no. 37; PM299

Probably after a version of the portrait closely similar to the one now in the Uffizi Gallery. Parker and Mathey hold that it was drawn from the painting originally in the collection of Prince Leopold–William in Brussels (Rooses 899). Whatever its origin this is a good example of Watteau's interpretation of Rubens into his own medium of *trois crayons*.

Lent by the Syndics of the Fitzwilliam Museum.

6 Design for a Fan-leaf

Bodycolour and watercolour, heightened with white, on brownish-grey Japanese paper; 216 × 425. Engraved by François Boucher, in reverse.
Provenance Charles Coypel (sale Paris, April 1753, 160); Bruzard (sale, Paris 23–26 April 1839, 300); the Paris branch of the Rothschilds; the English Rothschilds; Evelyn de Rothschild from whom it was purchased, 1965. 1965-6-12-1
Literature E. Croft-Murray, 'Watteau's Design for a 'Fan-Leaf', *Apollo*, xcix (1974), pp. 176–81.

As Croft-Murray points out this drawing is unique in Watteau's oeuvre as an example of his use of a variety of washes of both watercolour and bodycolour with white heightening. Otherwise, even his limited use of watercolours is extremely rare. A landscape drawing of Gentilly in the Teyler Museum, Haarlem (PM472) has greenish-grey washes and, most exceptionally, colour notes in Watteau's hand. Only one other design for a fan-leaf by Watteau is known, a red chalk drawing at Chatsworth (which, with the present drawing, was not included in Parker and Mathey's catalogue) but several such designs by Watteau have been recorded. The present drawing was engraved by Boucher for a set of engravings after Watteau, announced in *Mercure de France* in 1727.

The design is related to the painting *L'Amour au Théâtre italien* in the Berlin-Dahlem Museum (*K der K* 35) where the figures of Colombine and the old man leaning on a stick are closely similar. The two grotesque heads which flank the design above the main vignette are not related to any of Watteau's paintings though Croft-Murray sees a similarity between the female head on the right with that of a woman wearing a *fontange* in an early drawing (PM4) in a Paris private collection.

7 Landscape with Cottages and Figures

Red chalk; 167 × 239
Provenance Castelruiz. 1846-5-9-155
Literature G, p. 348, no. 5; P6; PM445

Dated by Parker and Mathey as perhaps 1712 and by Zimmermann in *K der K* as *c.* 1710, it is unquestionably an early drawing. As Parker and Mathey point out it has similarities with *Le Marais* (DV136) and *L'Abreuvoir* (DV137) which Mariette states were painted from nature at Porcherons where one of Crozat's estates was situated. Watteau was offered accommodation by Crozat perhaps as early as 1712 so that this drawing could date from that time. There is another very similar drawing of houses in the country (PM444), again probably done at Porcherons.

8 Standing Figure of a Friar, after an unknown Italian Master (?)

Black and red chalks; 227 × 183
Provenance Carpenter; Vaughan. 1900-8-24-159
Literature Lafenestre, pl. 27; P5; PM358

Considered by Parker and Mathey to be taken from an Italian master not identified. If so it has extraordinary vitality for a copy.

9 Seated Figure of an old Savoyarde with a Marmot Box

Two shades of red chalk and black chalk; 305 × 201. Engraved by Caylus, *Oeuvre de Caylus* (Bibliothèque Nationale), I, f. 216
Provenance Jullienne (sale Paris, 1767, 775?); Dimsdale (L2426); James (sale London, 1891, 310). 1891-7-13-5
Literature G, p. 311, no. 733; HV, p. 155; R. R. Tatlock, 'Two Watteau drawings', *Burlington Magazine*, XXXVIII (1921), pp. 156–7; P7; PM497

One of a set of popular types drawn by Watteau probably in 1710 or even earlier. On the *verso* is inscribed the beginning of a letter, in Watteau's hand, *Monsieur | . . . J'ay reçeu aujourd'huÿ au matin vos deux Lestres Ense[mble] | qui ont autant donne de peines au facteur qu'elles m' [ont] | Causés de surprise . . .* A more complete draft of the letter is found on the back of another drawing of the same figure, standing (Strauss collection, New York; PM496).

10 Studies of two Men dancing and of an elderly Man leaning on a Crutch

Red chalk; 173 × 228
Provenance James (sale London, 1891, 352). 1891-7-13-15
Literature G, p. 355, no. 64; Lafenestre, pl. 37; P8; PM84

The two dancers reappear in *L'Accordée de Village* (Soane Museum; *K der K* 19) and in *Le Contrat de Mariage* (Prado; *K der K* 33), while the study of the elderly man could have been used for the figure of Pantaloon in *Mascarade* (Hermitage; Camesasca 162) and was probably modelled on the comic actor, La Thorillière (1659–1731), of the Théâtre Français, of whom there are several studies, rather than on Watteau's friend the Abbé Haranger, as Parker at first suggested.

11 *Verso* Study of Plants and Grasses with Buildings in the Background

Black chalk and black wash; 183 × 238. Inscribed *3270* by Crozat, a register number (?)
Provenance Crozat (L2951); Dimsdale (L2426); James (sale London, 1891, 299). 1891-7-13-11
Literature Lafenestre, pl. 10; P9, fig. 5; PM476

A good and rare example of Watteau's use of wash, and even rarer among his extant drawing as a study of plants, the most conspicuous of which is a hart's tongue fern. The *recto* (PM43) has studies of three standing men, a man's head and three hands, used, except for the two hands at the bottom, for the painting *Qu'ay-je fait,*

Assassins maudits? (DV 150; Hermitage Museum). The style and attenuated character of the figures point to an early date, and it can probably be assumed that the *verso* belongs to the same period.

12 *Recto* Half-length Studies of a Man playing a Flageolet and of a Woman; a full-length Study of a Servant holding a Bottle and a Plate

Two shades of red chalk; 184 × 235
Provenance James (sale London, 1891, 321). 1891-7-13-13
Literature G, p. 353, no. 34; Lafenestre, pl. 30; P 10; PM 533

Only the study of the servant seems to have been used for a painting. The figure of a negro servant in the same posture is found in the engraving, *La Conversation* (DV 151); by J. M. Liotard after a lost original (Camesasca 108).

On the *verso* is a study of a tree in red chalk with washes of green and greenish brown. This is clearly executed from nature and the handling of the foliage is reminiscent of that found in the background of some of Watteau's pictures, e.g. *Les Confidences d'Arlequin* (*Wallace Collection*). See Walpole's rather contemptuous remarks on Watteau's trees in his *Anecdotes of Painting in England* (1786), IV, p. 74.

13 A comic Actor in Peasant's Costume

Red and black chalks; 338 × 187. Etched by J. Audran in *FddC* (202)
Provenance Raphael Ward. 1878-5-14-351
Literature Lafenestre, pl. 1; P 11; Parker 32; PM 910

The study for the compositional drawing in the National Gallery, Stockholm, in which the figure is reversed. This was engraved by Desplaces in *Figures françoises et comiques* with the title 'Poisson en habit de paisan' (DV 55). If it does represent Poisson it could be Philippe Poisson in the rôle of Blaise in Dancourt's comedy, *Les trois Cousines*. But Hérold and Vuaflart identify it as the actor Touvenelle (HV, p. 72), suggesting that the captions in *Figures françoises* relating to Poisson are inaccurate. Another very similar study, probably of the same actor, is in a private collection in Paris (PM 911).

14 An Oriental Servant walking, holding a Plate

Black and red chalk; 201 × 101. Etched, in reverse, by François Boucher (*FddC* 312). 1891-7-13-14
Provenance James (sale London, 1891, 344)
Literature Lafenestre, pl. 13; P 12; PM 793

The drawing is one of eleven of Orientals which can be connected with the arrival of a Persian embassy to Paris in 1715. Another similar drawing of the same model, standing in profile to the right, and bequeathed by Watteau to Caylus, is in the Teyler Museum, Haarlem (PM 794). An engraving of it by Audran was refused for *FddC*. The British Museum study is not known to have been used for a painting.

15 Fantastic Landscape

Red chalk; 222 × 360
Provenance L. C. G. Clarke; Sir R. Abdy. PD 106–1961
Literature PM 443

Caylus engraved a 'Titian' drawing, then in the French royal collection, representing the same landscape (Bibliothèque Nationale; *Oeuvre de Caylus*, I, f. 147). The present drawing differs from the engraving in various minor details.

The vertical, accented lines of the buildings and the way the leaning tree in the middle distance, left, is drawn, is so like details in some of Watteau's landscapes from nature and in his copies of the landscapes of older masters that Parker and Mathey's attribution of this drawing to Watteau seems well founded. Other rather similar landscapes are in the Ashmolean Museum (PM 441) and in the Bordeaux-Groult collection, Paris (PM 442). However, other details such as the vigorous use of 'toothed' chalk-strokes, particularly in the foreground, are less characteristic of Watteau and may be a reason for an attribution to Boucher which has been made for this drawing.

Lent by the Syndics of the Fitzwilliam Museum.

16 Studies of a Woman standing seen from Behind; a Woman half-length, her head in profile to the Left; Women's Hands

Red and black chalks and black lead; 165 × 225
Provenance Lempereur (L 1740); Utterson (L 909). 1857-2-28-213
Literature Lafenestre, pl. 24; P 13; PM 809

The style of the central study in particular suggests a fairly early date. These drawings are not known to have been used for any painting but the woman seen in profile has been identified by Parker and Mathey as probably one of the daughters of Sirois, the dealer and friend of Watteau. See also no. 24.

17 Head of a young Man turned three-quarters to the Right

Black and red chalks; 138 × 100
Provenance Purchased from Otto Goldschmidt.
1900-6-13-3
Literature P14; PM734

This study was not, so far as is known, used for a painting though there is a resemblance to the man seated in the centre of the group on the left of *Charmes de la Vie* (Wallace Collection; *K der K* 53).

18 Sheet of Studies: the half-length Figure of a Woman in Profile to Right and the Heads of three Women and a Man

Black, red and white chalks; 234 × 300
Provenance Lord Spencer (L1530; sale London, 1811); Vaughan (L1380). 1900-8-24-157
Literature Lafenestre, pl. 16; P15; Parker 62; PM615

The male head, and possibly the woman's head third from the left, may have been used for *L'Amour au Théâtre français* (Berlin, Staatliche Museen; *K der K* 34).

19 Four Studies of the Head of a young Woman, her Hair tied with a Ribbon

Two shades of red chalk and black and white chalks; 331 × 238
Provenance Utterson (L909; sale London, 1857); Robinson (L1433); Malcolm (L1489; JCR489). 1895-9-15-941
Literature de Chennevières, 'Les dessins des maîtres anciens exposés à L'École des Beaux-Arts', *Gazette des Beaux-Arts* (1879), p. 191, no. 474; Lafenestre, pl. 26; P17; Parker, pp. 12-13 and frontispiece; PM788

A similar sheet of studies of the same model is in the Bordeaux-Groult collection, Paris (PM783), of which there is a copy in the British Museum (which PM suggest could be by Demarteau who engraved it) and another is in the Forsyth Wickes collection, Boston, Museum of Fine Arts (PM786).

20 Head of a young Negro, inclined to the Left

Red, black and white chalks with touches of pastel, on greyish paper; 181 × 145
Provenance Woodburn (L2584). 1854-6-28-67
Literature G, p. 116; P18; PM727

This was clearly made *en suite* with the following study and does not appear to have been used for any of the paintings. A number of other studies of negroes by Watteau are known of which two are in the Louvre (PM729,730).

21 Head of a young Negro, inclined to the Right

Red and black chalks, with touches of rose-coloured pastel, on grey paper; 181 × 245
Provenance Woodburn (L2584). 1854-6-28-66
Literature G, p. 348, no. 3; P19; PM728

Though rather like the negro in the painting *La Conversation* (DV151), dated by Parker and Mathey not later than 1713, this is not the preparatory study which is in the Louvre (PM729).

22 A seated Woman turned to the Right, her Head looking down to the Front

Black chalk and black lead; 154 × 93. Etched in reverse by J. Audran (*FddC*152)
Provenance Utterson (L909, sale London, 1857); Robinson (L1433); Malcolm (L1489; JCR482). 1895-9-15-934
Literature Lafenestre, pl. 11; P20; Parker 36; PM623

The figure is reminiscent of the pose of one of the women in *Les Charmes de la Vie* (Wallace Collection; *K der K* 52) which was however taken from a study in the Louvre (PM825).

23 A Woman seated, seen from the Front, her Hands crossed

Pencil and red chalk; 155 × 94. Etched by François Boucher for *FddC* (266)
Provenance Utterson (L909, sale London, 1857); Robinson (L1433); Malcolm (L1489). 1895-9-15-934
Literature P21; Parker 34; PM601

The drawing was used for one of the figures in *Les Charmes de la Vie* (Wallace Collection; *K der K* 52).

24 Portrait Studies of the Heads of two of the Daughters of Sirois

Red and black chalks; 189 × 123
Provenance Utterson (L909); J C Robinson (L1433);
Malcolm (JCR490). 1895-9-15-942
Literature Lafenestre, pl. 21; P22; PM925

Both studies were used for the painting *Sous un Habit de Mezetin* (Wallace Collection; *K der K* 63). According to Mariette this represents Sirois, the dealer friend of Watteau, among his family. Whether this is so or not the two unidealized studies of women are certainly genuine portraits, and are reproduced with no modification of features in the painting. Mathey dates the studies 1718, Camesasca the painting 1717(?).

25 A seated Man playing the Violin seen in Profile to the left, wearing a Cape

Red and white chalks on light brown paper; 190 × 158
Provenance Rodgie. 1922-10-16-1
Literature Vasari Society facsimiles, 2nd series, v (1924), pl. 16; P23; PM816

None of the violin players in *Les Plaisirs du Bal* (Dulwich Collection; *K der K* 79) can be precisely identified with the study, though the one in the centre of the group of musicians could well have been taken from it.

26 Full-length Figure of a Man standing, wearing a *Tricorne* and holding a staff

Red chalk; 206 × 105
Provenance Salting (L2260). 1910-2-12-100
Literature P24; Parker 54; PM658

The figure reappears in *L'Embarquement pour Cythère* (Louvre; *K der K* 59) in the middle distance, left of centre. In the Berlin version of the painting (Charlottenburg Castle; *K der K* 69), the pose has been slightly modified and the lower part of the figure hidden. An enlarged study of the head of this figure is found in a sheet of studies in the Louvre (PM772) and must have served as the study for the paintings.

27 Studies of two Women turned to the Right, one holding up her Apron

Red and black chalk; 209 × 148
Provenance No record. 1846-11-14-23
Literature Lafenestre, pl. 34; P25; Parker 56; PM551

The lower figure appears in *L'Embarquement pour Cythère* (Berlin; *K der K* 69) and also in *Les Amusements champêtres* (DV126; Paris, private collection, Adhémar, pl. 101).

28 A Man helping a seated Woman to rise from the Ground

Red, black and white chalks on light brown paper; 336 × 226
Provenance James (L312; sale London, 1891, 312); Salting (L2260). 1910-2-12-98
Literature G, pp. 363-4; Vasari Society facsimiles, 2nd series, XI, (1930), pl.12; P. Lavallée, *Les dessins du XVIIIe siècle à la Bibliothèque de L'École Nationale des Beaux-Arts* (Paris, 1928), no. 4, pl. IV; E. Dacier, *Antoine Watteau* (Dessins de maîtres français, Paris, 1930), no. 52; P26, pl. 9; Parker 55; PM861

There are numerous studies for *L'Embarquement pour Cythère* (see also nos. 26, 27) but this is the most elaborate and the most arresting. The composition reappears almost unaltered as the pair to the right of centre in the Louvre painting, but somewhat modified for the male partner in the Charlottenburg version. It does not appear in *Figures de différents Caractères* but it may be deduced that Boucher particularly admired the composition as he introduced it on the easel at the foot of his frontispiece to volume II of *Figures de différents Caractères*. It is a particularly fine drawing and made the more vital by *pentimenti* and strong accentuations. Both Lavallée and Dacier describe a drawing at the École des Beaux-Arts, Paris, of a similar composition as by Watteau, but its quality is notably weaker and it is the work of an imitator.

29 Half-length Study of a Woman seen from Behind; Head of the same Woman looking three-quarters to Right

Red and black chalks; 232 × 163. Inscribed *3271*, bottom right, by Crozat
Provenance Crozat (L9961); James (sale London, 1891, 292); Salting (L2260). 1910-2-12-97
Literature P27, fig. 10; PM760

The study of the head may have been used for *L'Assemblée dans un Parc* (Berlin, Staatliche Museen; *K der K* 105). It has some similarities with Filloeul's engraving in *Livre de différents caractères de têtes* (Paris, 1752).

30 Head of a Young Woman, studied in Profile and in full Face

Red and black chalks; 173 × 156. The profile etched by L. Cars, in reverse (*FddC*261)
Provenance No record. 00-11-262
Literature Lafenestre, pl. 12; P28; Parker 44; PM776

The full face study was used in *Le Concert champêtre* (DV72).

31 Studies of a standing Man playing a Flute and of two seated Women facing Right

Red, black and white chalks; 253 × 375
Provenance Lord Spencer (L1530; sale London, 1811, 820). 1868-8-8-1274
Literature G, pp.349–50; Lafenestre, pl. 15; P29; PM605

The flautist was engraved by Audran and used for *Le Concert champêtre* (DV72) – for the costume and the posture of the figure – while another drawing (PM834) supplied the head and hands.

32 *Recto* Two seated Women, one in Profile to the Right and facing Front, the other with her Head in Profile to the Left

Red chalk and pencil; 145 × 191. Inscribed *3261*, bottom left, by Crozat
Provenance Crozat (L2951). 1846-11-14-25
Literature G, p. 349, no. 10; P30; PM602

On the *verso* is a very small, slight sketch of women and children, in red chalk. The woman on the right of the *recto* reappears in the painting *Amusements champêtres* (Wallace Collection; *K der K* 99) and again in the painting, very similar in composition, *Les Champs-Élysées*, also in the Wallace Collection (*K der K* 77).

33 A Woman in a striped Dress, seen from Behind, reclining on the Ground

Red and black chalks and pencil; 146 × 181. Etched, in reverse, by François Boucher (*FddC*161)
Provenance Utterson (L909; sale London, 1857); Robinson (L1433); Malcolm. 1895-9-15-936
Literature P31; Parker 69; PM610

The drawing was used for the figure in the centre of *Plaisirs d'Amour* (Dresden, *K der K* 89).

34 A Woman sitting on the Ground, seen from Above

Red chalk; 87 × 97
Provenance Utterson (L909; sale London, 1857). 1857-2-28-211
Literature Lafenestre, pl. 48; P32; PM583

Not used for any identified painting.

35 A Woman reclining, her Face in Profile to Right, with a Book in her Lap; Study of a Woman's left Hand

Red and black chalks; 134 × 95
Provenance James (sale London, 1891, 313); Salting (L2260–1). 1910-2-12-96
Literature P33; PM593

This may have been a preliminary study for a rather larger and more detailed drawing etched by L. Cars for *FddC* (185), where the posture is closely similar but in reverse. The original for the etching is not known.

36 A Woman seen from Behind sitting on the Ground, her Legs to the Right

Red, black and white chalks on brownish paper; 205 × 232. Etched by J. Audran, in reverse (*FddC*248)
Provenance James (sale London 1891, 325). 1891-7-13-4
Literature G 625; Lafenestre, pl. 4; E. Dacier, *Antoine Watteau* (Dessins de maîtres français, Paris, 1930), no. 14; P34; PM550

The drawing in the Louvre (33378), reproduced by both Dacier and Lavallée, is, according to Parker and Mathey, a copy of the present study, probably by the engraver Huquier whose mark appears on the sheet. He engraved arabesques as well as other usually summary or incomplete drawings after Watteau whose designs he completed or amplified. See PM, II, p. 27.

37 A Woman seated, looking to the Front, her right Arm outstretched

Black and red chalks with touches of white, on brownish paper; 207 × 165. Etched by François Boucher (*FddC*68)
Provenance Utterson (L909; Robinson (L1433; sale London, 7–8 May 1868); Malcolm (L1489; JCR486). 1895-9-15-938
Literature P36; PM626

The broad style of shading and accentuation, as well as the type of paper, are the same as in no. 38 and similar to a drawing in a private collection in Paris (PM 627), which may have been used for one of the figures in *La Perspective* (Boston, Museum of Fine Arts; Adhémar, pl. 56).

38 A Woman seen from Behind, reclining on the Ground, her Legs to the Left

Red and black chalks, with touches of white, on brownish paper; 145 × 162
Provenance Lawrence (L 2445); Robinson (L 1433); Malcolm (JCR 487). 1895-9-15-939
Literature P 35; PM 628

The study was certainly not used directly for any known painting but a similar silhouette appears among the figures in the background of *Les Charmes de la Vie* (Wallace Collection; *K der K* 52).

39 A seated Woman turned to the Right, her right Arm resting on a Ledge

Red and black chalks, the head worked over with the point of the brush and grey ink by a different hand; 149 × 117
Provenance Comte de Caylus (L 2919); Bacon (L 209). 1865-7-8-148
Literature Lafenestre, pl. 18; P 37; PM 625

The reworking on the head gives the study a curiously neo-classical appearance quite foreign to Watteau. It looks too as if another hand had strengthened certain parts with black chalk, for example the shadows of both hands, the area under the right arm, etc.

On the *verso* is a mutilated inscription by Caylus: [*Dessin qu*] *e Watteau a laissé en* [*mourant*] *a moy son ami. Caylus / 1721*. A similar inscription appears on the back of no. 40.

40 Portrait of a young Abbé, with a slight sketch, to the left, of a reclining female Nude

Black and red chalks; 148 × 230
Provenance Comte de Caylus; Rogers (sale London, 1856, 879); Breadalbane (sale London, 1886, 162). 1886-6-9-39
Literature Lafenestre, pl. 31; E. Dacier, 'Un ami de Watteau qui n'a jamais existé', *Revue de l'art ancien et moderne* (Paris, 10 July, 1921), p. 97; P 38; PM 930

The study is clearly for a portrait, a fact made plain not only by the personal qualities of the sitter revealed in the drawing, more clearly visible here than in many of Watteau's heads, but also in the black chalk framework enclosing it which was not added later as Hérold and Vuaflart believed (HV, p. 115).

The outline on the left has some affinity with the statue of a reclining woman in the *Réunion en plein Air* (Dresden; *K der K* 87).

An inscription on the *verso*: *Dessein que Watteau a laissé en mourant à moy son ami Caylus. Juillet 1721*, is similar to that on the back of no. 39 and is firm evidence that Caylus was one of the group of friends who were given some of the artist's work shortly before he died.

41 A Man in Profile looking to the Left

Red and black chalks; 138 × 98
Provenance Brisart (L 257); James (sale London, 1891, 348). 1893-12-12-2
Literature Lafenestre, pl. 40; P 39; PM 929

There is no evidence of the identity of the sitter, but he has generally been considered to be an abbé and he looks to be the same man as in no. 40. Parker suggests that he might have been Watteau's doctor as there is a medical prescription on the *verso* which reads: '. . . *de reglisse espluché et ensuite passé le tout en faites / cuire avec une livre et demie de sucre clarifié jusque a ce / soit en consistance de sirop. Vous metteré le dit sirop / . . . des bouteilles bien bouchées . . . / prendré trois cuilleres le soir et autant le Matin pendant / . . . ou quinze jours.*' This was doubtless prescribed for Watteau's cough for he was seriously ill with tuberculosis before he visited England in 1720. This study is likely to be a late work, c. 1720.

42 Commedia dell' Arte Actors

Red chalk; 169 × 184
Provenance No record. 1933-5-16-1
Literature K. T. Parker in *British Museum Quarterly*, VIII/2, (1933), pp. 1–3, pl. II; PM 876

This sketch is a rare example of a compositional study by Watteau. It seems to have been a first idea for his *Comédiens italiens* (DV 204) painted for Dr Mead in London about 1720. The painting is possibly the one which is now in the National Gallery, Washington. Two other compositional sketches connected with the picture are known, one in the Laughlin collection, Washington (PM 875), the other in the Musée Jacquemart-André, Paris (PM 873). The Washington sketch comes closest to the final composition. Though a drawing of Watteau's maturity, one characteristic derived from Gillot is still evident – the marked attenuation of the lower parts of the figures.

43 Three half-length Studies of a Man

Red chalk and pencil; 148 × 241
Provenance Malcolm (JCR 493). 1895-9-15-945
Literature P 40, pl. 3; PM 685

The centre study was used for one of the figures in *Réunion champêtre* (Dresden; *K der K* 87), while the figure leaning against an urn in *La Perspective* (Boston, Museum of Fine Arts; Adhémar, pl. 56) is reminiscent of the right-hand study.

44 Head of a Man with Eyes lowered and Head tilted back

Red and black chalks; 100 × 89
Provenance Lawrence (L 2445, sale London, 1835); Richardson (L 2183); Malcolm (L 1489; JCR 488). 1895-9-15-940
Literature P 41; PM 724

A head drawn in a similar pose but with the eyes turned upwards (PM 726) is in the Metropolitan Museum and is a study for the painting *Mezzetin playing a Guitar* (Metropolitan Museum; *K der K* 41).

45 Head of a Woman looking towards the Left; Head of a small Dog

Black and red chalks; 147 × 143
Provenance Utterson (L 909; sale London, 1857, 647); Robinson (L 1489); Malcolm (JCR 481). 1895-9-15-933
Literature Lafenestre, pl. 36; HV, pp. 67-8; P 42; Parker, p. 22; PM 739

Hérold and Vuaflart consider the woman standing next to the figure of Gilles in the composition *Les Comédiens italiens* (DV 204), for which this head is a study, to be the actress, Helena Balletti, known as Flaminia (1686–1721). The painting which Baron engraved (DV 204) was originally in the collection of Dr Mead and is possibly the one now in the National Gallery, Washington (Camesasca 203). The dog's head is a study for *Retour de Chasse* (DV 19).

46 *Recto* Three Studies of open Hands

Red and black chalk and pencil; 148 × 225
Provenance Deffett-Francis (L 1447). 1875-6-12-558
Literature Lafenestre, pl. 42; P 43; PM 827

The left-hand and centre studies were used for *Les Comédiens italiens* (DV 204) as was the red chalk drawing on the *verso* of a man raising a curtain (PM 682). Watteau's drawings of hands, whether they are separate studies, of which there are numerous examples, or the

hands of his musicians, actors or models are often among his most beautiful and characteristic work.

47 Two Studies of a Man playing a Guitar; Study of a Man's right Arm

Red, black and white chalks on brown paper; 244 × 379
Provenance Lord Spencer (L 1530, sale London, 1811, 821); White. 1868-8-8-1275
Literature G, p. 350, no. 16; Lafenestre, pl. 33; P 44, pl. 5; Parker 91; PM 830

The left-hand study was used for *La Gamme d'Amour* (London, National Gallery; *K der K* 124; and *L'Assemblée dans un Parc* (Berlin; *K der K* 105); and the right-hand study for *La Perspective* (Boston; Camesasca 117, pls. IV–V). The study of the arm is for *Les Comédiens italiens* (DV 204).

48 A seated Woman; two Studies after Sculptures of Putti playing with a Goat

Red chalk, touched with white, on brownish paper; 222 × 376
Provenance James (sale London, 1891, 302). 1891-7-13-2
Literature G, pp. 351-2, 364; Lafenestre, pl. 25; P 45; M. Digard, *J. M. Sarazin*, 1934; PM 334

According to Goncourt the group of sculptures was made by Sarazin for Marly but its location is not known today. However, its pendant, a similar work, is in the Louvre. The study in the centre seems to have been used for *L'Assemblée dans un Parc* (Berlin; *K der K* 105), and the right-hand study for *La Cascade* (Paris, private collection; copy in the Wallace Collection), engraved by Scotin (DV 28).

49 Small Girl, seen from Behind, right Knee on the Ground

Red chalk; 134 × 100
Provenance No record. 1859-6-11-98
Literature G, p. 349, no. 11; P 46; PM 695

Though there are weaknesses in the drawing the attribution is hardly in doubt for the figure is found in *Divertissements champetres* (Wallace Collection; *K der K* 98, 99) and also in *L'Amour paisible* (DV 268).

50 A Woman seated with a little Girl on her Knee; another Child standing to her Right

Red and black chalks heightened with white; 241 × 161. Etched in reverse by François Boucher (*FddC* 238 for the woman and child, 228 for the standing girl).
Provenance James (sale London, 1891, 203); Joseph. 1891-6-27-152
Literature Lafenestre, pl. 28; P 47; PM 706

Boucher made another etching of the standing child seen from the front (*FddC* 85). None of these studies seem to have been used for a painting. A good example of Watteau's late manner with rapid lines of sanguine very boldly strengthened with black chalk and lightly heightened with white.

51 Half-length Figure of a Man wearing a *Tricorne* and looking Left; Study of a Man's Hands holding a Basket

Red and black chalk, heightened with white, on light brown paper; 255 × 178
Provenance Lord Spencer (L 1530; sale London, 1811, 823). 1869-6-12-297
Literature G, p. 248, no. 6; Lafenestre, pl. 46; P 48; PM 721

It has been pointed out by Parker and Mathey that the hands appear to have been joined to the body by another draughtsman, and that originally there had been two independent studies. The hands of a woman in precisely the same pose are found in Tardieu's engraving after Watteau, *Les Champs-Élysées* (DV 133) but are in reverse in the painting of the same composition in the Wallace Collection (*K der K* 77, 78).

52 A half-nude Woman seated on a Chaise-Longue and holding her left Foot in her Hands

Red and black chalks on white paper; 341 × 221
Provenance Jullienne (?); Ottley (L 2664; sale London, 1838); Lawrence (L 2445); Woodburn (L 2584). 1860-6-16-136
Literature G, p. 349, no. 13; L. Binyon, 'Les dessins de Watteau au British Museum', *Revue de l'art ancien et moderne* (July–August 1921), p. 138 (with reproduction); Lafenestre, no. 39; P 49, fig. 7; Parker 83; PM 526

The large sloping characters in pencil of the inscription *Watteau*, bottom left, are similar to the hand of Jullienne.
    One of a group of nude drawings of the same model posed on a chaise-longue. Caylus in his address to the Academy in 1740 implied that Watteau did not really understand the nude and lacked a knowledge of anatomy. Some of his studies of male nudes (of which the British Museum has no example) show Caylus's opinion to be false. It is true however that in his female nudes Watteau was more interested in the texture and suppleness of the flesh than in the underlying structure of bones and muscles.

53 A nude Woman sitting on a Chaise-Longue, holding a Shift

Red and black chalks on bluish-grey paper; 225 × 254
Provenance James (L 2260-1; sale London, 1891, 327); Salting. 1910-2-12-99
Literature G, p. 364; P 50; Parker 82; PM 523; Saint-Paulien, 'L'oeuvre de Watteau', *Watteau*, ed. Jean Ferré (Madrid, 1972), 1, p. 62

The study was used for the painting *La Toilette* (Wallace Collection; *K der K* 50). There was also a study for the head of the woman between the curtains in the background of the picture in the James collection from which the present drawing originally came.
    A recent writer, Saint-Paulien, has commented adversely on the quality of this drawing – in the right leg, the neck, and the face which he considers heavily reworked.

54 An Engraver working at his Table

Red chalk; 235 × 304
Provenance Hugh Howard (L 2957, sale London, 1873); Earls of Wicklow. 1874-8-8-2279
Literature G, pp. 347–8; P 51; Parker 96; PM 913

Goncourt states that there was an inscription on the *verso* in Howard's hand, *M. Baron, the graver, by A. Watteau*, but this no longer exists and was probably removed with the old backing to the drawing. Baron, a French engraver working in London, would have been twenty-three when Watteau visited England, 1719–20. Hérold and Vuaflart thought that Watteau here portrayed someone much older than this, and suggested the engraver Dorigny. In fact it is difficult to be sure how old the engraver as drawn might have been. It is not even certain that the drawing was made in England for the fleur-de-lys watermark indicates either a French or Dutch paper.

55 Two half-length Studies of a young Woman wearing a linen Cap and turned to the Left, one showing her Face in Profile, the other the Back of the Head

Black and red chalk; 291 × 171
Provenance Marchetti (L2911); Lord Somers (L2981); Robinson (L1433); Malcolm (L1489; JCR491). 1895-9-15-943
Literature L. Binyon, 'Les dessins de Watteau au Musée Britannique', *Revue de L'art ancien et moderne* (Jul.–Aug. 1921), p. 146; P52, fig. 11; Parker 97; PM785

Parker first pointed out that the watermark in the paper is English (the coat-of-arms of the City of London) and that it is therefore almost certain that the drawing dates from Watteau's stay in England, 1719–20. Parker also attributes the Italian inscription, *Singulari diseg.ni di Vato*, on the *verso*, to the collector Gaburri and believes that the sheet was sent to him by Mariette on behalf of Jullienne.

The style is sparse and linear and the lines distinctively angular as sometimes found in Watteau's late studies of the less highly-finished kind.

56 An allegorical Scene: *Le Naufrage*

Red chalk; 223 × 340. Engraved by Caylus, in reverse (DV182), with the caption, *LE NAUFRAGE, gravé d'après le dessin original de Watteau*
Provenance Douce. Ashmolean Museum 559
Literature S. Colvin, *Drawings in the University galleries* (1907), iii, pl. 39; K. T. Parker, *Catalogue of Drawings in the Ashmolean Museum*, I (1938), pp. 269–70, no. 559; PM853

The drawing is exceptional, both as an allegory and because it can be dated with some precision. It is generally taken to represent Watteau's rescue from financial 'shipwreck' by Jullienne. Jullienne was able to save 6,000 livres belonging to Watteau from the collapse of Law's bank in 1720, a short time after the former's return to France from England. The stormy scene may also be a reference to the Channel crossing. The style of the drawing is strikingly 'rococo'.

Lent by the Visitors of the Ashmolean Museum.

Offsets

57 A Couple walking Arm in Arm to the Left

Offset in oil colour; 245 × 162
Provenance Vaughan. 1900-8-24-161
Literature Vasari Society facsimiles, 1st series, III (1907–8), no. 34; Lafenestre, pl. 7; P54; PM867

One of a small number of offsets from brush drawings in oil, probably preliminary oil sketches for the paintings with which they are known to be connected. This example is closely related to figures in *L'Amour paisible* (Charlottenburg Castle, Berlin; Adhémar, pl. 142). Both figures also derive from known drawings, the man from a sheet of studies in the Louvre (PM668) and the woman from a study in the Musée des Arts Décoratifs, Paris (PM631).

58 Three half-length Studies of a Woman with Ribbons in her Hair; a Woman's Arm holding a Fan

Offset in red, black and white chalks; 305 × 214
Provenance Lawrence (L2445); Woodburn (L2584). 1860-6-16-137
Literature Lafenestre, pl. 6; P55; PM786 (note)

Goncourt considered this to be an original drawing. It is in fact an offset of the studies in the Forsyth Wickes collection, Boston, Museum of Fine Arts (PM786). The model is the same as in no. 19 and the heads drawn in a closely similar way.

The top figure of the original was used for *La Gamme d'Amour* (National Gallery, London; *K der K* 124) and *L'Assemblée dans un Parc* (Berlin; *K der K* 105).

59 Four studies of male Figures

Offset in red and black chalks; 157 × 236
Provenance Raphael Ward. 1870-5-14-350
Literature G, p. 350, no. 17; P57

The man with the staff seems to have been taken from a sheet of three figures in the Städel Institute, Frankfort (no. 1047), a study for one of the pilgrims in the *Ile de Cythère* (DV155; *K der K* 29). The figure more faintly offset, to the left of the man with the staff, is also connected with another pilgrim in the same painting.

Biographical Notes

1684   10 October: Jean-Antoine Watteau baptised in the church of Saint-Jacques, Valenciennes.

c. 1699   Apprenticed to Jacques-Albert Gérin, a Valenciennes painter.

c. 1703   In Paris. Earns a living painting heads and devotional figures for a contractor supplying the provincial market.

Frequents the print shop of Pierre Mariette II and his son Jean.

Here perhaps first meets the artist Claude Gillot and begins work with him.

c. 1707   Becomes assistant to Claude Audran III at the Palais de Luxembourg.

A student of the Academy (Académie Royale de Peinture).

1709   6 April: selected by the Academy as a candidate for the Prix de Rome, but fails to win it.

About this time returns to Valenciennes and works on military subjects.

1710   Back in Paris. Stays with Sirois at his shop on the Pont Notre-Dame.

1712   30 July: declared *agréé* by the Academy. Meets Pierre Crozat who offers him accommodation and the freedom of his collection.

1714   5 January: reproved by the Academy for not submitting his admission piece.

1715   5 January: again reproved.

Crozat returns from Italy with many new acquisitions. Watteau's second stay with him.

13 June: is visited by Count Tessin, Swedish statesman and collector.

1716   5 January: again called to order by the Academy.

22 December: Crozat writes to the artist Rosalba Carriera of Watteau's ability as an artist.

1717   28 August: Watteau admitted to the Academy with his *Embarquement pour Cythère*.

1719   First notice of Watteau in *L'Abecedario Pittorico* of Pellegrino Antonio Orlandi (new edition).

Travels to London where he stays for some months and paints for Dr Mead by whom he may have been treated for his illness (?tuberculosis).

1720   By the late summer back in Paris, his condition worsening.

21 August: visited by Rosalba Carriera.

Probably starts work on and completes *L'Enseigne de Gersaint*.

1721   Rosalba Carriera paints Watteau's portrait and Watteau draws hers.

On account of his illness moves to Nogent-sur-Marne, to one of Crozat's houses. Paints landscapes.

Feeling himself dying arranges for the sale of his paintings and distributes drawings to his friends: the comte de Caylus, Crozat, Jullienne, Hénin, the Abbé Harenger and Gersaint.

18 July: Watteau dies.

6

I

3

5

4

2

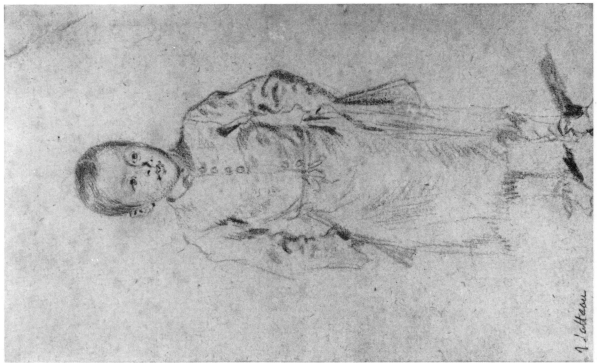

Ant. Watteau

7

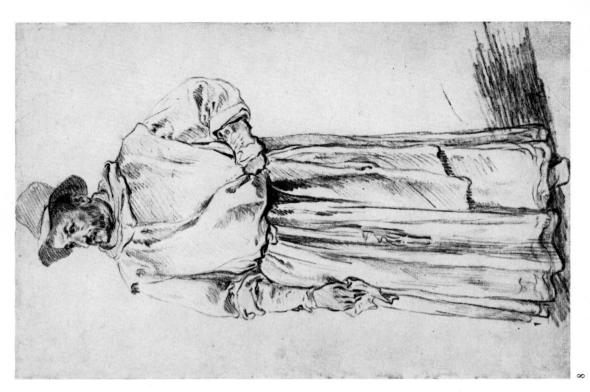

8

9

II verso

19

11 *recto*

20

21

12 verso

14

23

22

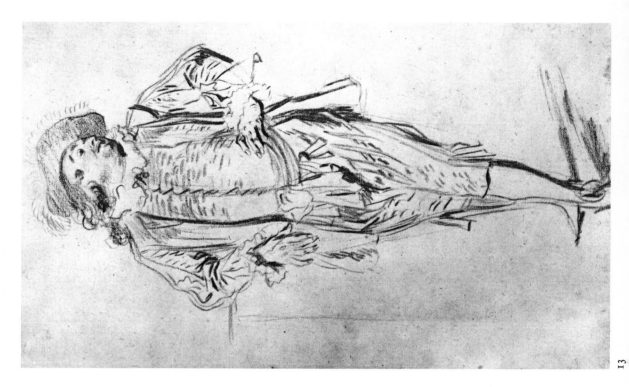

13

10

12 *recto*

16

18

25

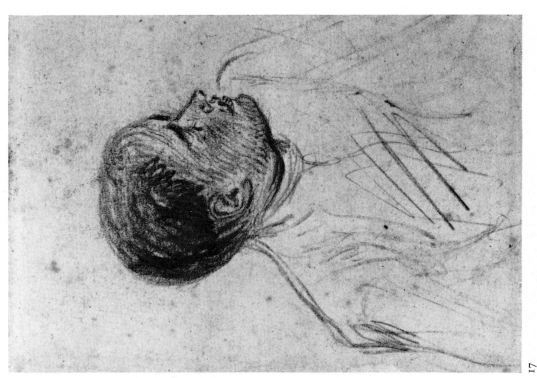

17

24

28

26

27

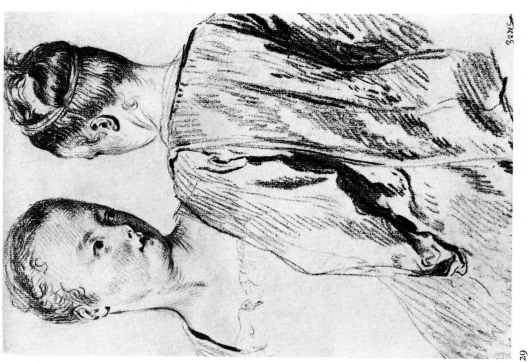

29

50

32 verso

34

33

3.283

32 recto

30

35

31

36

37

39

42

38

46 *verso*

43

48

47

41 verso

57

51

49

44

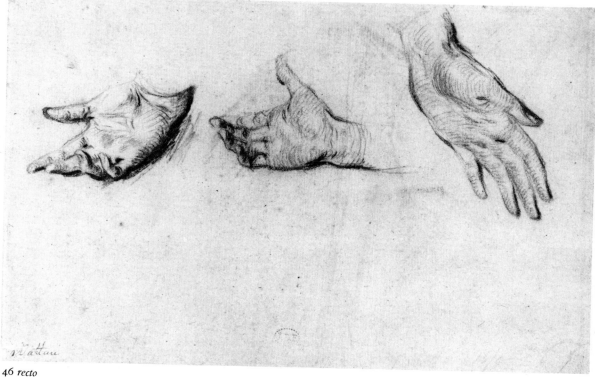

46 *recto*

41 *recto*

45

56

53

52

58

55